Happy Bi

By Janice Behrens

ISBN: 978-1-338-88854-6

Editor: Liza Charlesworth
Art Director: Tannaz Fassihi; Designer: Tanya Chernyak
Photos ©: 5: Stefan Stanisavljevic/Getty Images; 6: juliannafunk/Getty Images; 7: DEMIURGE_100/Getty Images; 8: Burke/Triolo Productions/Getty Images. All other photos © Shutterstock.com.

1 2 3 4 5 6 7 8 9 10   68   31 30 29 28 27 26 25 24 23

Printed in Jiaxing, China. First printing, January 2023.

SCHOLASTIC INC.

Get the birthday hats.

Get the birthday presents.

Get the birthday balloons.

Get the birthday plates.

Get the birthday cake.

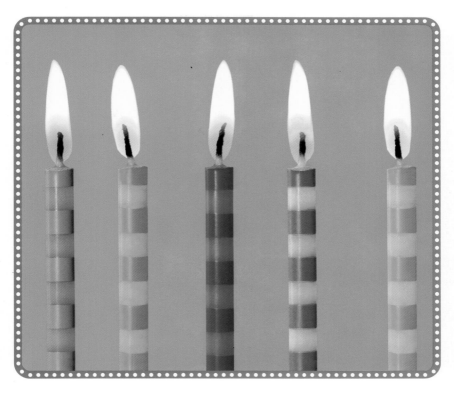

Get the birthday candles.

Happy birthday!